FRANKENSTEIN

NOW AND FOREVER

MW00325237

LOOK AT THAT! IN THE FOUNTAIN CITY, RESIDENTS GET EVICTED BECAUSE OF EXPENSIVE AND POINTLESS RENOVATIONS. ON THE PAVEMENT, EVERYTHING THEY HAVEN'T TAKEN... SOON TO BE PICKED UP BY OTHERS... TO TAKE UP NEW SPACE...

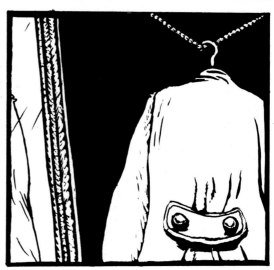

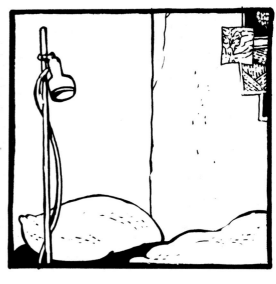

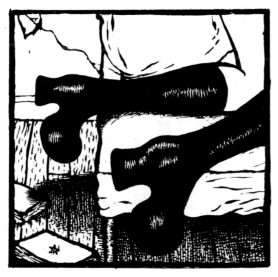

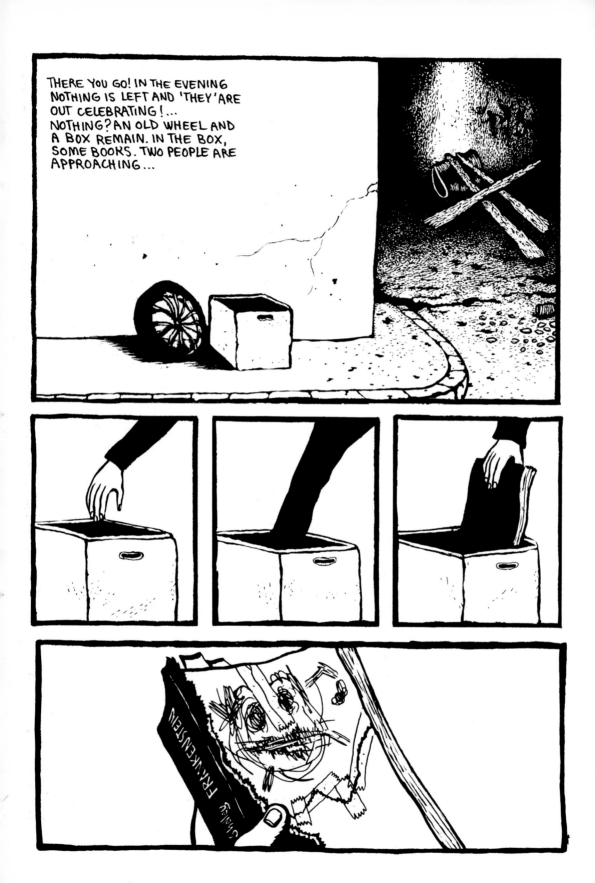

I'VE HEARD THAT "FRANKENSTEIN" WAS WRITTEN AROUND HERE...

YEAH... THE STORY IS SET HERE TOO.

...REALLY? I THOUGHT IT HAPPENED IN PRAGUE OR SOMETHING...

NO, EVA, THAT'S "THE GOLEM"

AH... COULD BE...

PRAGUE HAS ITS GOLEM AND HERE WE'VE GOT FRANK-ENSTEIN'S CREATURE!! ...

THAT CREATURE'S FIRST MURDER... WHAT ABOUT IT? ...

WELL... HE STRANGLED DR. FRANKENSTEIN'S LITTLE BROTHER ...

THEY SEARCHED FOR THE KILLER... THE CREATURE ESCAPED... JUSTINE, THE SERVANT, WAS ACCUSED INSTEAD.

...TSS... ANOTHER GRAVE MISCAR- RIAGE OF JUSTICE IN THIS TOWN ...

YEAH, THAT ABOUT SUMS IT UP!

BUT WHY'S THE MONSTER...I MEAN... THE CREATURE-WHY'S HE SO BAD? ...

HE'S ANGRY...

ACTUALLY, IN THE BEGINNING HE IS VERY GENTLE, AND THEN... EVERYTHING GOES WRONG.

WHEN HE SEES WHAT HE'S CREATED, DR. FRANKENSTEIN IS TERRIFIED AND RUNS OFF...

THE CREATURE, LEFT TO HIMSELF, WANDERS THE STREETS OF INGOLSTADT, WHERE THE DOCTOR HAD STUDIED AND CARRIED OUT HIS EXPERIMENTS...

THE CITIZENS OF INGOLSTADT CHASE HIM AWAY BECAUSE OF HIS HORRIBLE APPEARANCE...

AND THEN... I THINK... HE HIDES IN THE FOREST AND LEARNS HOW TO SURVIVE... ALONE...

HE COMES ACROSS A COTTAGE. IN IT LIVES A FRENCH FAMILY.

HE WATCHES THEM CONSTANTLY, NOT DARING TO SHOW HIMSELF AFTER WHAT HAS HAPPENED.

ONE DAY THE FAMILY HAS A STRANGE VISITOR...

A YOUNG ARAB WOMAN.

ARE YOU KIDDING? THERE ARE NO ARABS IN "FRANKENSTEIN"!!

SURE THERE ARE... THOUGH IN FACT SHE'S HALF TURKISH...

HUH?

YEAH... HER MOTHER, A CHRISTIAN ARAB, WAS A SLAVE OF THE TURKS... BUT ONE OF THEM FELL IN LOVE WITH HER AND MARRIED HER...

IN PARIS HE ENDED UP IN PRISON, HE WAS THE VICTIM OF A PLOT...

ALL BECAUSE OF HIS RELIGION...

AH...THAT BOOK'S JUST FILLED WITH INJUSTICE ...

UH-HUH...

...AND THE CHARACTERS GET FLAYED ALIVE!! SHOULD I CONTINUE, EVA? ...

GO ON... FOR ONCE I'M INTERESTED IN SOMETHING ...

UMM... THE FRENCH FAMILY TRIED TO HELP THE YOUNG TURKISH WOMAN ...

... THEY TAUGHT HER TO SPEAK, READ AND WRITE FRENCH...

OISEAU
ARBRE
FLEUR

THE CREATURE, WATCHING, LEARNS IT TOO... HE LEARNS QUICKLY...HE WORSHIPS THAT FAMILY...

ONE DAY THE BLIND OLD FATHER WAS ALONE AT HOME...

WHO IS THERE? ... COME IN !!!

BY YOUR LANGUAGE, STRANGER, I SUPPOSE YOU ARE MY COUNTRYMAN; ARE YOU FRENCH? ...

NO; BUT I WAS EDUCATED BY A FRENCH FAMILY AND UNDERSTAND THAT LANGUAGE ONLY.

I AM GOING TO CLAIM THE PROTECTION OF SOME FRIENDS, WHOM I SINCERLY LOVE, AND OF WHOSE FAVOUR I HAVE SOME HOPES ...

ARE THEY GERMANS? ...

NO, THEY ARE FRENCH

BUT LET US CHANGE THE SUBJECT. I AM AN UNFORTUNATE AND DESERTED CREATURE ... I LOOK AROUND AND I HAVE NO RELATION OR FRIEND UPON EARTH. THESE AMIABLE PEOPLE TO WHOM I GO HAVE NEVER SEEN ME AND KNOW LITTLE OF ME. I AM FULL OF FEARS, FOR IF I FAIL THERE, I AM AN OUTCAST IN THE WORLD FOREVER ...

DO NOT DESPAIR. TO BE FRIENDLESS IS INDEED TO BE UNFORTUNATE; BUT THE HEARTS OF MEN, WHEN UNPREJUDICED BY ANY OBVIOUS SELF-INTEREST, ARE FULL OF BROTHERLY LOVE AND CHARITY. RELY, THEREFORE, ON YOUR HOPES; AND IF THESE FRIENDS ARE GOOD AND AMIABLE, DO NOT DESPAIR ...

THEY ARE KIND ...

... THEY ARE THE MOST EXCELLENT CREATURES IN THE WORLD; BUT, UNFORTUNATELY, THEY ARE PREJUDICED AGAINST ME. I HAVE GOOD DISPOSITIONS; MY LIFE HAS BEEN HITHERTO HARMLESS AND IN SOME DEGREE BENEFICIAL; BUT A FATAL PREJUDICE CLOUDS THEIR EYES, AND WHERE THEY OUGHT TO SEE A FEELING AND KIND FRIEND, THEY BEHOLD ONLY A DETESTABLE MONSTER ...

FOR CHRISSAKE! WHEN'S HE GOING TO TELL THEM THEY'RE HIS FRIENDS?

RIGHT... WAIT... THE OLD MAN SAYS

HE WANTS TO HELP HIM ...

HEY, EVA! THIS THING IS TOTALLY INSANE... EVA? ARE YOU ASLEEP? THERE'S SOME SORT OF DIARY WRITTEN WITH A PENCIL ON THE PAGES OF THE BOOK ...

Mmm...

I WONDER WHAT THE PREVIOUS OWNER OF THIS BOOK MUST HAVE BEEN LIKE IT GIVES ME THE CREEPS ...

ZZr rZZZ

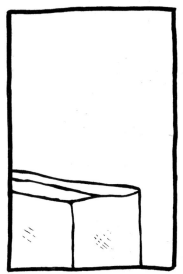

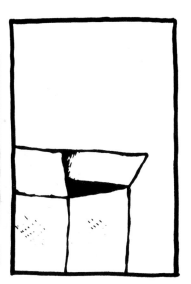

...WELL...WE'RE ALL A BIT PIECED TOGETHER ... WE'RE ALL AN ASSEMBLY ...UH... OF MEMORIES...OF DEAD AND FORGOTTEN EVENTS AND THEREFORE DEAD?... UM... AND THEN UH... PFF... WE'RE ALL FROM DIFFERENT BACKGROUNDS AND...YEAH IN SHORT, AN ASSEMBLY... YES?

HUM?

HEYYY...

WHAT'S ALL THIS BULLSHIT?...I'VE NEVER HEARD SUCH NONSENSE!! ...MMH...

thud

WELL... OKAY...YOU'RE RIGHT...IT WASN'T A GREAT EX- PLANATION...

STILL, IT'S NICE OF YOU TO TRY TO CONSOLE ME... BUT YOU SEEM TO BE AFRAID... THAT UPSETS ME ...

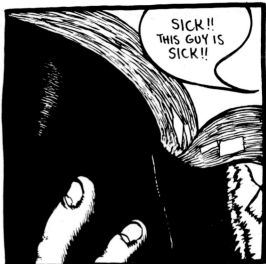

SICK!! THIS GUY IS SICK!!

...AND THEN THOSE BROWN STAINS ON EVERY PAGE... WHAT THE HELL IS THAT? IS IT BLOOD OR WHAT?

SHIT... CAN'T TOUCH THAT THING ANY MORE... IT'S TOO UGLY...

HIS HAND-WRITING IS TOO HARD TO READ ANY-WAY...

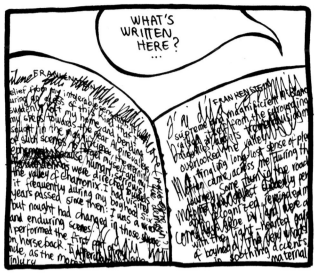

RIGHT...UH...
NO NEED TO
DWELL ON THAT
PAGE...

IT'S ALL
CRAZY
STUFF
ANYWAY!!
...

FLAP
FLAP

FLAP
FLAP

HEY,
WHAT'S
THAT ??
...

A
PHOTOGRAPH?

HMM...I THINK
I'VE SEEN THIS
GUY BEFORE...
IN TOWN
...

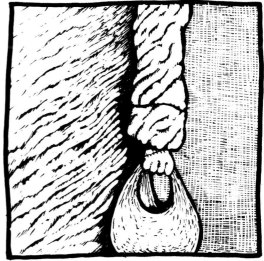

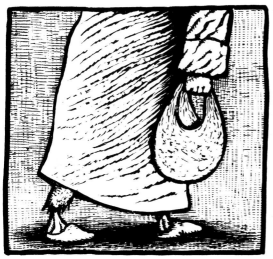

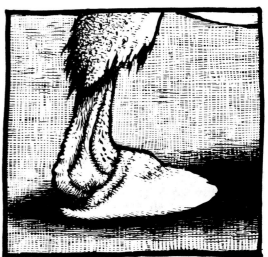

A PICTURE OF SOMEONE'S BACK... THE KIND OF PICTURE MICHEL USED TO TAKE...

...YEEES! DEFINITELY... MICHEL...

I REMEMBER...HE HAD A WHOLE COLLECTION OF THOSE PICTURES! HE KEPT THEM IN NOTEBOOKS... OLD EXERCISE BOOKS...

THAT'S THE LAST ONE I TOOK...DO YOU LIKE IT?

SURE...IT'S OKAY. BUT WHY DO YOU ALWAYS TAKE PICTURES OF PEOPLE'S BACKS?
...
BECAUSE IT'S EASIER?
...

WELL... IT'S CERTAINLY EASIER... GIVEN I ALWAYS PHOTO-GRAPH STRANGERS IN THE STREET... THIS WAY, THERE'S NO NEED TO ASK THEIR PERMISSION...

BUT THAT'S NOT THE REASON...I DO IT BECAUSE I LIKE THE IMAGE... IT MAKES THEM...I DON'T KNOW... MYSTERIOUS... OR...UH... MELANCHOLY?
...
WELL
...

SOMETHING LIKE THAT.

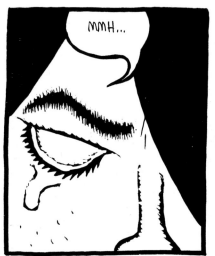

plic
plic

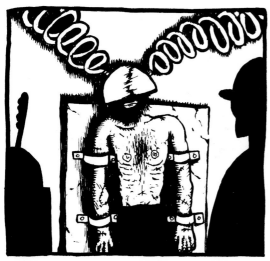

RIGHT... MUST STOP
IMAGINING THINGS!
...

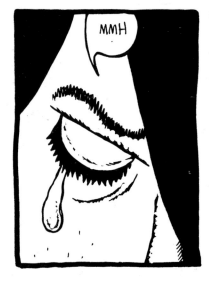

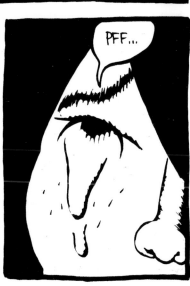

DAMN...DAMN. DON'T BE STUPID...I CAN FEEL IT COMING ON... MUSTN'T HAVE ANOTHER BREAKDOWN... NO...

CONCENTRATE!... KEEP MY EYES OPEN!...

EYE OPEN...

CUISINE ▶

JUST LOOK AT WHAT'S IN FRONT OF ME ...

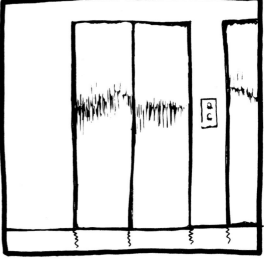

Aumonerie catholique

Soins intensifs chirurgicaux

Cuisines

CMU

thermique

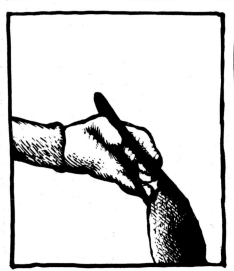

OVER AND DONE WITH.

OKAY. I WON'T LET THAT CRAP GO TO MY HEAD.

HEHEHEEE

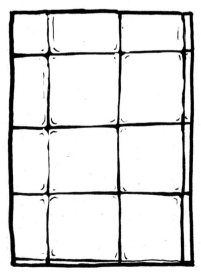

I REMEMBER A FACE... OF A CHARACTER...

OF COURSE! THAT BOOK WE FOUND YESTERDAY...

I HAD A DREAM ABOUT FRANKEN-STEIN'S CREATURE...

GOT TO FOLLOW HIM!

STILL HAVEN'T SEEN HIS FACE...

PERHAPS IT'S
BETTER IF I
DON'T SEE ...
HIS FACE...

I SHOULDN'T
FOLLOW HIM
...
I SHOULD
GO TO SLEEP...
FORGET IT ALL.

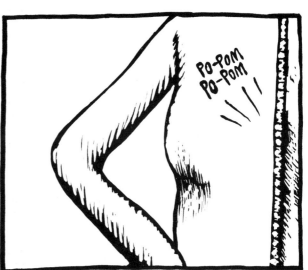

WHAT DOES IT MEAN?

DID HE LEAVE IT **FOR ME** OR WHAT? IS IT INTENDED FOR ME?

HOLD ON... HOLD ON... HE JUST FORGOT HIS BAG... THAT'S ALL.

ANYWAY... I'M IN LUCK. I'LL HAVE A LOOK INSIDE AND PUT MY MIND AT EASE ...

TANGIBLE PROOF THAT I'M FILLING MY HEAD WITH BULLSHIT...

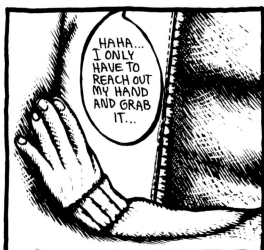

AAAAAAAAAHH

HAHAHA

...TOO STUPID!

...
I'LL WALK HOME... FORGET IT ALL...

HUM

...CANT STOP WONDERING WHAT WAS IN THE BAG ...

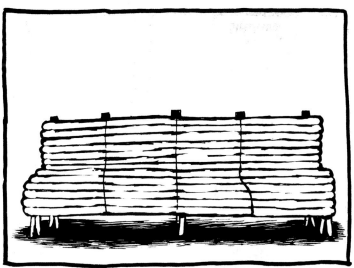

THE CLIMATE HERE IS ONE OF THE WORST TO LIVE IN!

...WHEN I SAY "CLIMATE" I'M NOT JUST THINKING ABOUT THE WEATHER ... IN ANY CASE, IT FOSTERS DEPRESSION ... YES...

I'M SURE THAT'S THE REASON I'M IN THIS STATE... OTHERWISE... WHY WOULD I BE LIKE THIS?

AND WHY DO I STAY HERE?

MUST BE OFF!

I HAVE THE FEELING THAT ONLY THIS CITY COULD HAVE PRODUCED...

First Printing: February 2005
ISBN: 0-9549308-0-0
Printed in Canada

"Frankenstein encore et toujours" © 2001 Atrabile
English edition © 2005 Typocrat Press
Published by Nadia Katz-Wise and George South
Translated by Arthur van Kruining and Richard Lawson
Production by Nadia Katz-Wise and George South
Designed by Steven Preston

All rights reserved. No part of this book may be re-
produced (except small portions for review purposes)
without expressed written consent from Alex Baladi or
Typocrat Press.

Typocrat Press, 3 Hackney Road, London, E2 7NX, UK
Email: info@typocrat.com

www.typocrat.com